A Walk Down Phonics Lane

Walking with Nature

Cherie Feemster

Illustrator: Jasmine T. Mills
ISBN Number: 978-0-578-67033-1

This book is dedicated to the loving memory of my mother Edna Elizabeth Jackson. Thank you for being the amazing role model of a woman, mother, and educator. Thank you for showing me that what you desire you can do all you have to do is do it!

Phonics Lane is a special place to me, whether walking or picking **A**pples from the apple trees, or kicking the **B**rown rocks that are on the ground.

Watching creatures **C**rawling all around, some

Dangling from branches, waving to us all as we

walk down phonics lane.

Oh, the sounds of the **Earth** and nature are everywhere, **Filling** my ears with so much joy! The hummingbirds **Flying** away with twigs and green **Grass**, preparing their nests for the little ones to come.

I say "**Hello**" to all that are helping me to see and enjoy more and more of the beauty surrounding me.

Inside the big and small trees hide the **J**umping squirrels and chipmunks playing hide and seek from me. But me being **K**ind and not wanting to disturb their fun, I continue to walk quietly down Phonics **L**ane.

Looking down on the ground, I see a **Mirror**

showing me a beautiful picture. Oh my!

It's a picture of me!

Over and over the sounds of **N**ature continue to ring for me to **P**icture them again and again and again. When suddenly, I hear **Q**uacking from both the geese and **t**he ducks as I begin to sit near the pond.

Under the clouds and the sunshine,

I take a moment to rest and think

about all the colors that I saw.

Violet, **W**hite, and **Y**ellow,

just to name a few. It has

been exciting to walk down

Phonics Lane today, and

tomorrow I will ride to

the Phonics **Z**oo.

Will you come with me there too?